This book belongs to:

Deirdre
Our friendship
makes me Happy
in my Heart
—Rhonda
Dec 2021

P.S.
My cousin
Nicole wrote
this book

For my Dixon Kids

ISBN: 978-0-57888727-2 (Hardcover)

Printed in U.S.A.

FIRST EDITION, 2021.

Happy in my Heart

story by **Nicole Dixon**

illustrated by **Maria Mughal**

Enjoy those special
moments that make you
Happy in your Heart
Nicole Dixon

Mommy always says,
"I'm happy in my heart."

What does that mean?
I ask.

"It's that moment when something
special makes
your face shine bright,
your body feel warm,
and love wraps you up
in a great big hug."

What makes you happy in your heart?
I ask.

"It's anything and everything, big or
small. A place, a person, a feeling,
or a smile."

"It's that moment that makes
your face shine bright,
your body feel warm, and love wraps
you up in a great big hug."

What kinds of things? I ask.

"Remember when we drove to the country and picked our very own berries and came home and baked a beautiful olallieberry pie?"

"That made me happy in my heart."

"Remember when we created
beautiful chalk drawings
on the sidewalk
to inspire our neighbors,
and they stopped
to take pictures?"

**"That made me
happy in my heart."**

"Remember those early mornings snuggling on the couch with a purring kitten?"

"That made me happy in my heart."

"Remember going
for a long drive
listening to our favorite music
and singing
as loud as we could?"

**"That made me
happy in my heart."**

"Remember eating
sweet treats
like ice cream or cupcakes
and
giggling with friends?"

**"That made me
happy in my heart."**

Sweet Treats

Cupcakes
Chocolate
Vanilla
Rose Velvet
Lemon Blackberry

Mini Cupcakes
Chocolate
Vanilla
Strawberry Swirl
Frostfetti

Donuts
Maple Bar
Old Fashion
Glazed
Bear Claw
Rainbow Sprinkles

Cakes
Lemon Custard
German Chocolate
White with Strawberries
Angel Food Cake
Chocolate Fudge

"Remember our
favorite beach getaways,
the early morning
walks along the shore,
getting our feet wet
and searching
for sand dollars?"

**"That made me
happy in my heart."**

"Remember all your games, races, musicals, and theater performances I watched?"

"That made me happy in my heart."

"Remember dinner picnics
with the whole family
at our favorite
secret park?"

**"That made me
happy in my heart."**

Oh, I think I understand, I say.
Like right now with you, Mommy!

Remembering all these special things
we did, and seeing you smile!

This moment makes my face shine
bright, my body feel warm, and love is
wrapping me up in a great big hug!

…and Mommy said,
**"That makes me happy in my
heart!"**

Can you think of a time when you were Happy in your Heart ??

_____

_____

_____

_____

_____

_____

About the author

Nicole Dixon is married and a Mommy to three kids, and lives in Campbell, California. She loved reading  books to her children at bedtime and always thought it would be fun to write about those special moments that made her **Happy in her Heart.**

CPSIA information can be obtained
at www.ICGtesting.com
Printed in the USA
LVHW070855010621
689024LV00030B/2587